Indigenous Religious Therapeutics:

The Legal Basis for Religious Based Indigenous, Traditional and Native American Complementary and Alternative Medicine and Modalities and
The Right To Express Them

Ethical, Legal and Practical issues
for
NAIC Ministers &
Indigenous CAM Practitioners

By

Anthony B. James

Indigenous Religious Therapeutics:

"The Legal Basis for Religious Based Indigenous, Traditional Native American Complementary and Alternative Medicine and Modalities and The Right To Practice and Express Them"
Sub Title: Ethical, Legal and Practical issue's for NAIC CAM Practitioners.

Metta Journal Press: 5401 Brooksville, FL 34602

Ebook ISBN 13: 978-1-886338-31-9
Print Edition ISBN 13: 978-1-886338-32-6

- Developed by Dr. Anthony B. James DNM(P), ND, MD(AM)
- NAIC/ SMOKH Ordained Minister Practicing Spiritually based "CAM", Chirothesia Healing and Indigenous Medicine for 38 years
- Educational Director NAIC: SomaVeda College of Natural Medicine

This course will cover a broad view of principles and guidelines for the legal basis for Indigenous, traditional and Native American "CAM" and Chirothesia or Spiritually based therapies in the US. The information is valuable for both Licensed and unlicensed ministerial and or religious practitioners at all levels of expertise and education.

Topics

- This course will cover:

  - **Four Systems, Four Umbrellas**
  - **Secular Umbrella**
  - **Religious Umbrella**
  - **Native American Umbrella**
  - **American Indian Religious Freedom Act of 1978**
  - **Expressive Private membership Association**

  - What's the Best Way to Go?
  - Alternative Medicine or Spiritual Medicine?
  - At the Very Least Do No Harm
  - Alternative Healthcare Practices are not the Practice of Medicine
  - What is Chirothesia?
  - What does Chirothesia mean?
  - Chirothesia Healthcare
  - –Our Approach is Different!
  - –What is Health?
  - –Historical Antecedents
  - –Informed Consent
  - –Exceptions and Exemptions from Medical Licensing
  - –Private Membership Association
  - –Ethics and Practice
  - –Structuring Your Practice
  - –Your Web and Internet Use
  - –The Forbidden Words
  - –Summary
  - –Resources

Four Systems, Four Umbrellas

The four systems to legally practice CAM and Natural Medicine in the USA include:

- **Secular:** Under the Jurisdiction of Governmental Regulation of Federal and State Law or Statute

- **Religious:** Under the Sovereign Jurisdiction of Ecclesiastical, Church and or Religious Authority per Church Law or Code

- **Native American:** Under the Jurisdiction of Sovereign Native American Tribal and or Religious Affiliation (NAC-Native American Indigenous Church etc.)
  Expressive Private Association Membership: (Private Association of Church Members)

1: Secular Umbrella

Medical and Allied Medical Laws, Boards of Regulation and Vocational Statutes and rules. Peer Reviewed Scope of Practice and Standards

Definition of Secular: *Under the Jurisdiction of Governmental Regulation of Federal, State, County and City Law or Statute.*

- Medical Laws for Various Specialties (Allopathy, Osteopathic, Chiropractic, Nursing, Physical Therapy, Psychology, Psychiatry, LCSW, Nutritionist, Acupuncture etc.)

- Allied Medical and or Secular Vocational License Laws and Boards for Various Specialties

  - (Massage, Massage Therapy, Dietician, Esthetics etc.)

2.

Religious/ Ecclesiastical Umbrella

Based on Separation of Church and State
Provisions of Constitutional, Federal, State and
Supreme Court Decisions establishing the
Autonomy and Sovereignty of Ecclesiastical
Authority to be Self Regulating.

**Under the Jurisdiction of Non-Governmental
Regulation**
Ecclesiastical, Church and Religious Authority
Law or Statute as defined by scripture, indigenous
and or native traditions, sacred texts and
members RPG's, as well traditional roles and
responsibilities.

Courts will refuse to hear based on jurisdiction!

What healing ministries have churches offered commonly for thousands of years?

1. Tending, Healing, Counseling, Ministering to the Lame, Sick and dying (Medicine, Therapy, Counseling), Casting our Demons (Psychology, Mental Health Counseling and Therapy) has always been accepted as a common use and practice of spiritual societies.

2. **Religious Institutions can issue:** Degrees, Licenses, Ordinations and Commissions for various specialties within the expressed theology. A therapeutic ministry may include any and all-natural therapies and remedial arts as proscribed by Bible, Sacred Text, Doctrine, Dogma, Tradition, Family and common practice. Provided according to level of education and expressed authority of the religious body.

3. These protections are not exclusive. They cannot prejudice or prefer one religion over another for protection.

4. NAIC is an Integrated Auxiliary of the Priory of Saving Grace. The Priory of Saving Grace is Priory #110 of the Sacred Medical Order of The Church of Hope (SMOCH/ SMOKH). The Church of Hope is a Church of special and sacred ministry of monastic medicine, sanctified healing, ecclesiastical medicine, holistic medicine, as well as indigenous medicines as part of our religious doctrine. SMOCH/ SMOKH is a Diocese of the Eastern Apostolic Orthodox Catholic Church of the Americas: Chaldean- Syrian Rite. SMOKH is the Medical Arm of the EAOC.

5. Dr. Anthony B. James is formally recognized as a Priest, Chaplain of Holiness, Monsegnor by EAOC Americas, blessed and ordained by the Father Mar Basilius Adao Perrera: Patriarch of the Americas and Brazil. As such he is empowered to form religious communities under the church.

6. Dr. Anthony B. James is formally recognized as a Priest, Monsignor, Licentiate Monastic Medical Doctor by SMOKH, blessed and ordained by the Church of Hope. As such he is empowered to form religious communities under the church.

3. Native American Umbrella

Under the Jurisdiction of Sovereign Native American Tribal and or Religious Affiliation (NAIC-Native American Indigenous Church)

Not Secular: Not under the Jurisdiction of Governmental Regulation of Federal, State, County and City Law or Statute.

A) Indian Religious and Civil Freedoms Act
The **American Indian Religious and Civil Freedoms Act**, Public Law No. 95-341, 92 Stat. 469 (Aug. 11, 1978) (commonly abbreviated to AIRFA), codified at 42 U.S.C. § 1996, (1)

B) Religious Land Use and Institutionalized Persons Act of 2000 June 2, 2005, 106th CONGRESS, 2d Session S. 2869: www.somaveda.com/religious-act/
(4)

Federal Laws Stating No Governmental Authority, Federal, State, and City etc. has the right to regulate the practice of Native American Medicine and Traditional Spirituality and its expression and ceremony at all! Applies to all tribes equally. Membership. Roles and specifics vary from tribe to tribe.

Native American Indigenous Church Inc. (NAIC) An expressed private membership association for medicine, healing, curing and life. NAIC is open for Non-ethnic, non-blood quotient Indian/ persons to join.

The American Indian Religious Freedom Act

Along with the subsequent amendments, make it very clear that all American Native people of federally recognized tribes, along with bona fide incorporated, tribal organizations such as Native American Church (Native American Indigenous Church) are qualified for the exceptions to all laws of the United States that concern the American Native Culture (American Native Tribal Spiritual Leaders and Spiritual Leaders of Native American Church, est. 1918).

August 11, 1978, Public Law 95-341, 92 Stat. 469
95th Congress - Joint Resolution
American Indian Religious Freedom
[S.J. Res. 102]

Resolved by the Senate and House of Representatives of the United States of America in Congress assembled, That henceforth it shall be the policy of the United States to protect and preserve for American Indians their inherent right of freedom to believe, express and exercise the traditional religions of the American Indian, Eskimo, Aleut, and Native Hawaiians, including but not limited to access to sites, use and possession of sacred objects, and the freedom to worship through ceremonials and traditional rites.

American Indian Religious Freedom. 42 USC 1996. (Amended 1994)

"To amend the American Indian Religious Freedom Act to provide for the traditional use of peyote by Indians for religious purposes, and for other purposes. Be it enacted by the Senate and House of Representatives of the United States of America in Congress assembled,"

4. Expressive Private Membership Association Umbrella

Pro's:

Governed under legal principles of: <u>Rights of Members</u>

- Freedom of Association

- Freedom of Speech

- Right to Privacy

- Contract Law

- Supreme Court Decisions at both Federal and State level.

- Various Lower Court Rulings

Cons:

If <u>Secular,</u> it's Not Bulletproof!

- Subject to change according to changes in statute or other court rulings.

Can be challenged- sued in court.

Corporate Veil can be pierced (Not easy, but it is possible)

Must be an active member of the Association

- Following all of the RPG's, Code of Ethics and Scope of Practice Rules. Violation and or non-compliance = NO Protection!

What's The Best Way To Go?

SECULAR:

- If your practice is secular, corporate, State Licensed Medical and/or *without spiritual* and or energetic basis (belief or faith in the unseen)

ECCLESIASTICAL:

- If your practice is spiritual, religious, religious therapeutic, energetic, based on a *faith in the unseen* and or on natural, elemental, traditional, sacred, holy or divine text and principles or If you're a Medicine Elder/ Person: Man or Woman, Pastor, Clergy, Priest, Monk, Minister, Cleric, Shaman or Rabbi or the equivalent then go Ecclesiastical.

Expressive PRIVATE Association:

- If you can't make up mind, and you are ok to take a chance! Keep in mind, protections are limited, and you have to follow the club RPG's! See "Rights of Members"

Best. A layered Legal Umbrella!

• An Expressive Private Membership Association, organized within and under the authority of an Ecclesiastical Jurisdiction (Church i.e. SMOCH/ Priory of Saving Grace), which is also a Native American Indigenous Religious Tribal Organization, which meets Federal Statute legal protections (AIRFA, RLUIPA) for the belief and expression of Native American Religion and it's practices and which under US Code is given the patent right to self-determination as to what the specific Tribal Organization beliefs, practices and expressions shall consist thereof..

Ministry is an expression of a sincere and firmly held conviction that healing and the practice of religious therapeutics is an expression of Indigenous, Native American and Christian Sacradotal Duties as expressed in Mathew 10:8 as expressed by Jesus the Christ and To protect the practice of Mother Earth based Native American spiritual traditions, beliefs, ceremony, sacred practices, expressions, Indigenous and Natural Medicine ways.

S.M.O.CH.

Practitioner is Ordained and or Licensed Minister/ Monastic Medical Practitioner by Church.

3
N.A.I.C. Expressive Private Membership Association Or equivilent with your own Independent Branch or Auxiliary ALL= 100% Services are for MEMBERS ONLY! No exceptions!

Practitioner is Authorized and or Ordained Minister/ Medicine Person by Tribal Org.

Informed Consent
4
All communicants, members required to sign and witness Ministry Informed Consent. No Consent signed = NO SERVICES!

Legal Umbrella

"Alternative Medicine" or Chirothesia/ Spiritual Medicine

- Alternative healthcare practices can be generally defined as Religious Therapeutics, Traditional Chirothesia, Spiritual, Religious, Energetic, Vitality, Pastoral, Ministerial, Clerical, Tribal, Indigenous Native, Familial or other practices:

  - That are used by individuals, often for self-help,

  - To achieve and maintain a healthy status,

  - Either on their own or complimentary to standard medical care

  - As an expression of Indigenous and Native Culture

- These practices **do not** include the potentially dangerous use of invasive techniques and toxic drugs that are the province of licensed medicine.

At the Very Least "Do No Harm"

- Alternative medicine and therapeutic practices:
    - **Do include** developing therapies and non-standard approaches that are outside of the scope of practice of secular licensed medicine.
    - **Do not include** the potentially dangerous use of invasive techniques and toxic drugs that are the province of licensed medicine.

- These practices in general are sometimes referred to as "Complementary and Alternative Modalities" (CAM) or **Chirothesia**, Religious Therapeutics, Natural Medicine, Naturopathy, Spiritual Healing, Sacred Healing etc.

Also known as *Indigenous (clerical/ pastoral/ ministerial) Healthcare, Healing Science, Counseling and Medicine* (IHSM)

Alternative and or Chirothesia Healthcare Practices are NOT the Practice of Medicine!

Let me say it another way. Alternative, Chirothesia, Pastoral, Clerical, Ministerial, Tribal healing, wellness and health care practices are NOT the practice of medicine as defined by State Medical Practices acts. Therefor NOT the practice of "Medicine" and not under purview, sight, supervision, or jurisdiction of ANY governmental authority by patent right of exception granted by AIRFA and RLUIPA and the various state statutes that affirm AIRFA and RLUIPA! There are NO LOOP HOLES! (This is NOT a "Sovereign Citizen Movement" thing.) This statement is based entirely on the strictest reading of the afore mentioned US Code establishing and protecting Native American Religious expression and practice and US Church law from Constitution to various State Code affirming religious rights of expression, including but not limited to US Tax code.

- [Practitioner/ Member] does not diagnose or prescribe for neither medical nor psychological conditions nor claim to prevent, treat, mitigate or cure such conditions.
    - (As defined by secular practices acts)

- [Practitioner/ Member] does not provide diagnosis, care, treatment or rehabilitation of individuals, nor apply medical, mental health or human development principles.

  - (As defined by secular practices acts)

Etymology: What is "Chirothesia":

- **Chi** = (Pronounced Ki as in Kite) In original meaning: is the place where God's law is taught.

- **Chiro** connotes the "hand" Laying on the Hands, the imposition of the hands to direct or deliver divine and or healing energy. (alt. Cheiro Gr root cheir 'hand') Traditionally refers to the Orthodox Greek rites of ordination and healing ritual or ceremony practiced between an ordained priest or minister and a communicant.

- **Thesia** (fr. Thesis) denotes a setting, placing or to do.

- **Theos** "of or pertaining to God"

Chirothesia means:

- **Chirothesia** = Literally means "Led by the healing hand of God".

- **Chirothesia** interpreted is the practice of therapy, healing or blessing transmitting and communicating the divine energy (energia, vital life force, chi, prana, orgone, ki, huna, holy spirit, breath etc.) led by the healing hand of God.

- **Chirothesia Practitioners** (Chirothesist, Therapeutae, Minister, Clergy, Priest, Medicine Person, Rabbi etc.) are understood to literally be the Hands of God administering healing in the material world.

- Chirothesia is a ritual act of passing divine or healing energy, awareness, consciousness, breath and pressure to another as a religious or spiritual act or observance.

"Laying on Hands" used around the world:

Examples included in this would be all the worlds' major faiths such as Islam, Buddhism, Sikh, Baha'i, Huna and Native American Indigenous and or Traditional Medicine including Peyote and Ayahuasca ceremony as well as other plant based native sacraments.

- In Christian churches, this practice is used as both a **symbolic** and **formal method** of invoking the Holy Spirit: during baptisms and confirmations, healing services, blessings, and ordination of priests, ministers, elders, deacons, and other church officers, along with a variety of other church sacraments and holy ceremonies.

Chirothesia is a religious duty:

- Jesus the Christ was a Chirothesist. In the New Testament the laying on of hands was associated with the receiving of the Holy Spirit (See Acts 8:14-19). Initially the Apostles laid hands on new believers as well as believers. (See Acts 6:5-6).

- In the early church, the practice continued and is still used in a wide variety of church ceremonies. The belief is that the practice of Chirothesia can have curative properties, based on biblical precedent set by Jesus, who would walk for days, offering his healing power.

- Both Christian and non-Christian healers of faith will lay hands on people when praying for healing, and often the name of Jesus or of some other saintly person is invoked as the spiritual agency through which the healing of physical ailments is believed to be obtained.

Chirothesia is a Religious Therapeutic CAM practice:

In modern terms, Religious Therapeutic CAM practices of Chirothesia based modalities can be defined as:

- Elegant, comprehensive and sophisticated protocols that work for the remedy and alleviation of pain and suffering, healing the sick and injured of spirit, mind and body administered during ceremony or as church authorized sacrament by or between church members and or ministers as a healing and or restorative practice. (Mother Earth, Mind, Body, Spirit integration)

Chirothesia Healthcare:

Also known as *Indigenous (clerical/ pastoral/ ministerial) Healthcare, Healing Science, Counseling and Medicine* (IHSM)

- Includes developing therapies

- Non-standard approaches that are outside the scope of licensed medicine.

- Such approaches as: (Examples only, not limited to…)

  - Nutrition, Homeopathy, Hands-on-Healing, Magnetics, Sound therapy, Polarity, Somatics, Energy Therapies, Reflexology, Biofeedback, Meditation, Breath Work, Reiki, Chi Gung, Tai Chi, Herbology, Iridology, Tapping, Aromatherapy, Balneotherapy, Light therapy, Massotherapy, Vibration and Crystal Healing, Mantra, Chakra Balancing, Smudging, Religious Therapeutics, ceremonial and or ritual healing etc.

  - Traditional Chinese, Classical Indian Ayurveda, Islamic Yunani, Filipino Hilot, Indigenous and Traditional Native American Medicine and or folk remedies and "Grand Ma Doc" home remedies are also examples of CAM practices.

  - These practices aim at more efficient psychological, emotional, energetic, physiological and spiritual integration and function of the human organism, leading to optimal wellness.

- Spiritually based natural health care is often misunderstood understood within the law. Conventional medicine and holistic health care use different paradigms. In some ways they are miles apart. The newer holistic paradigm does not fit neatly into the present legal structure of health care in America. That structure is defined mainly by the state medical practice acts.

- The shift in health care paradigms is causing confusion in the legal realm, as legislators attempt to fit the old concepts into the new reality. One reason for the membership, disclaimer, disclosure and consent forms recommended for use is to help you define the paradigm or framework in which you practice. This will avoid confusion, create more realistic expectations, and protect both practitioner and client.

Religious Therapeutics

What are Religious Therapeutics?

"The idea of religious therapeutics embraces principles and practices that support human well-being with recognition of the common ground and cooperation of health and religiousness. Dimensions of religious therapeutics include the following:

- Religious meanings that inform philosophy of health and medicine
- Religious means of healing
- Health as a support to religious life
- Religiousness itself as a remedy for the suffering of the human condition

(Religious Therapeutics: Gregory P. Fields: State University of New York Press, Albany, NY 2001)

It establishes traditional models for the relations between health, healing and the practice of specific religions and can designate specific principles and practices such as therapeutic prayers, meditations, rituals and physical interventions for healing.

The literal meaning of the word **Heal** taken from the original Old English verbal root *hal* is "To Make Whole".

Heal or to make whole means to restore from a bad condition and literally means to save from, to purify, to cleanse and to repair or restore from evil, pernicious, suffering or unwholesomeness. It means to correct to harmony, to correct to a right relationship restoring to wholeness that which is out of balance. To heal is to correct or have corrected that which is out of communication with true essence, nature, spirit and soul. To remove or reduce any impediments to self-realization, oneness with God, Spirit and Soul by any means necessary.

The word *therapeutic* is from the Greek *therapuein* and means curing and restoring. *Therapeia*, healing, connotes religious or medical endeavors, for it refers to the attending of a healer to a patient (one who suffers) and also designates "attending" in the form of religious ministering. (Ames, "The meaning of Body in Classical Chinese Philosophy," is *Self as Body*, ed. Kasulis et al., 158)

`Curing refers to alleviating impaired functioning and discomfort or whatever interferes in your process of pursuing spiritual elevation and practice, self-realization or inner peace and integrity of being.

Restoring is returning to an original state of integrity, wholeness and well-being or oneness of spirit, mind and body. Each in balance according to its nature and function.

Being one, being true and clear, being well, being happy, being able to participate fully in life in spiritual pursuit, having experience of Love, Compassion, Joy and balanced mind and removing impediments, restoring what is broken or lost and the knowledge, practice and technique used to do these things is religious therapy.

Native Traditions of Healing:

- **From the beginning of time** when people first walked, Great Spirit provided human beings with two indigenous spiritual ceremonial customs that honor the two earthly substances that sustain Human life: Air (Father Sky) and Food (Mother Earth) – Sacrament (Peyote, Ayahuasca, San Pedro, Tobacco, Sweet Grass, Sage and other sacred herbs and plants used in healing ceremony such as Cannabis, Yage etc.).

- Partaking of these two sacred gifts, our first parents, first supplied by the Great Spirit they then evolved into other ceremonial customs. These ceremonies from the beginning to the present manifested themselves from the promptings of ones' heart. It has been discovered that the regular practicing of these ceremonies enhances the participant member, worshipers' ability to walk in, Faith, Gratitude, Humility, Charity, Respect, Honor and Forgiveness.

- Over centuries these basic observances were expanded to incorporate all sacred healing practices and sacraments honoring Mother Earth.

- Practicing and living these ceremonies on a regular basis tend to enhance and assist one to live with honor and respect for all their relations that leads to a responsible and peaceful existence

- All of the following ceremonies remain with us today, due to the courage and tenaciousness of our indigenous ancestors. Throughout human history there have been influences based in greed and prideful intentions that have sought to destroy or marginalized the practicing of these Sacred Ceremonies.

Through these trials and tribulations, Native American Indigenous Church has established a **Code of Ethics and Ceremonial Protocols and training** to sustain these ancient religious practices for generations upon generations to come.

Native Traditions of Ceremony and Healing

- **1. The Birth Ceremony**– honors the passing into a new existence of all earthly beings.

- **2. The Sacred Breath ceremony**– Two important purposes for this ceremony are 1) to have the Great Spirit infiltrate every cell of one's body and 2) to assist the participant experience unconditional love.

- **3. The Holy Anointing (Laying on of Hands Ceremony)** – American Native Spiritual Leaders have traditionally used the natural power of touch to accomplish healing, empowerment and creation to connect with our creator (Divine Touch).
Throughout history and today Medicine People are aware of the effects of touch with the essences of plants, oils and herbs on the body, mind and emotions.
   Native people and NAIC use touching as a religious therapeutic intervention. They utilize touch and fragrance of seeds, roots, barks, flowers and leaves in ritual healing, empowerment and creation. NAIC Members are free to use any method they are trained, certified, authorized and or blessed to use. Native Healers are free to share, exchange and or utilize the indigenous, traditional medicines of any tribe. We honor the healing traditions of not just or exclusively North American Tribes and peoples but those of all native peoples without discrimination.

- **4.** **The Marriage Blanket** – honors the public and open commitment of two or more people to serve the human family unit for life and all eternity.

- **5.** **The Passing On of Spirit Ceremony** – honors the passing of any earthly beings into the next realm of Existence.

- **6.** **The Potlach Ceremony**– (Trade Blanket) Distribution of Wealth and Wopela (Sacred eating, feasting and sharing of natural bounty).

- **7.** **The Sacred Pipe (Casuse and or Chanupa) Ceremony** – Four important purposes for this ceremony are:
  - **1)** Remind the participants to honor and respect the power of prayer
  - **2)** assist in unity and respect of male and female differences
  - **3)** activate the law of synergy to assist all participants in achieving their heartfelt desires
  - **4)** Tobacco is a messenger herb/ spirit assisting to manifest our intentions in real life. (Also, why Tobacco use is potentially harmful!) Any herb or plant can be utilized in this ceremony according to tradition. (Bearberry, Chan Sha Sha etc.)

- **8. The Sacrament Ceremony–** (Using Sacred substances derived from all nature: Fire, Earth, Water, Wood... Plant, Mineral, Air in a blessed way according to specific Native, Tribal Organization traditions) Five important purposes for this ceremony are:

  - **1)** to rediscover one's innate goodness **2)** assist in the forgiveness process for oneself and others

  - **3)** to reside in truth unified with all nature

  - **4)** to cleanse the Spirit, Mind, Body and life of harmful energies and those elements which obstruct one from a direct, productive and meaningful relationship to spirit

  - **5)** to commune directly with our makers.

- **9. The Spirit Dance–** A celebration of the Millennium and living in gratitude.

- **10. The Sun Dance (Fire Dance) –** Sacrifice oneself for the people and to lead a life of service.

- **11. The Sweat Lodge (Amacheekee/ Inipi) Ceremony** Three important purposes for this ceremony are 1) remind the participants they are children of mother earth 2) assist the participants to honor and respect all of one's relatives, especially one's biological mother and father. 3) Purification and remediation of past negative thought, action and deeds.

- **12. The Vision Quest (Hanblecheyapi) Ceremony** – Fasting/ Crying for a Vision: enables human beings to re-remember and understand the mission that they had previously committed to achieving before their spirit assumed its earthly body. Connects one to the essence of nature within them.

- **13. Traditional Biblical based Natural Healing and Natural Medicines.** These practices which are coherent with and supportive of the true spiritual nature of human beings living in loving harmony with the Divine, Mother Earth and Each Other. The NAIC recognizes the Human Right to access to Mother Earth/ "Pancha Mama" based natural and spiritual healing regardless of its source or origin.

Native and or Indigenous/ Aboriginal/ Tribal/ Familial Traditions of Healing are Legal!

- Legal precedence dictates that the Native American Indigenous Church has full Constitutional Rights and Protections as have **ALL** other registered Churches, worshipping in the United States of America since September 17, 1787.

   1) Priory of Saving Grace (Under Sacred Medical Order of the Church of Hope- SMOKH, a Diocese of the Eastern Apostolic Orthodox Catholic Church of the Americas: Chaldean- Syrian Rite).

- **2)** Native American Indigenous Church INC a Florida State Chartered Not-for Profit Corp: A Religious Tribal Organization practicing Indigenous, natural medicine as a genuine, authentic and traditional expression of the practice of Native American/ Aboriginal religion.

- **3) NAIC is an IRS 501(c)3 Compliant, Tax Exempt, Religious/ Church Organization according to IRS Code**

- **Exemption:** Recognition of Tax-Exempt Status: *"Automatic Exemption for Churches that meet the requirements of IRC section 501(c)(3) and or 508(c)1(A) are automatically considered tax* *exempt and are not required to apply for and obtain recognition of tax-exempt status from the IRS."* Copied verbatim from IRS 501(C)3 Tax Guide for Churches and Religious Organizations. (Page 3, Second Paragraph)

- **4) AIRFA (American Indian Religious Freedoms Act) (RLUIPA)**

- **5) Religious Land Use and Institutionalized Persons Act of 2000**

- **6) 42 USC Chapter 21- Religious Freedom Restoration Act**

- **7) PROVIDERS DECLARATION OF NINTH AMENDMENT RIGHTS**

-

- **8) NAIC ARTICLES OF RELIGIOUS PRACTICE, EDUCATION AND HEALTHCARE MEMBERSHIP** (5)

- **9) NAIC Authorized Participant Membership Approval and Agreement** (6)

- **10) State Medical and Massage Board Exemptions for Native, Ecclesiastical/ Religious/ Church Practitioners** (7)

- **Gonzales vs. O Centro Espirita Beneficente União do Vegetal** (9)

- **The Boyl Decision** (10)

INTERNATIONAL TREATY AND DECLARATIONS: Establishing religious freedom and access to traditional medicine as human rights.

Under United Nations Treaty and Convention

1) **Universal Declaration of Human Rights**

2) **Declaration of Alma Ata**

Our approach is different!

It is very important to understand the different health paradigms. Otherwise it may be difficult to understand how legislators approach health care regulation.

What is Health?

Health is "a state of complete physical, mental [spiritual] and social well-being and not merely the absence of disease or infirmity. The definition seeks to include social and economic sectors within the scope of attaining health and reaffirms health as a **human right**."

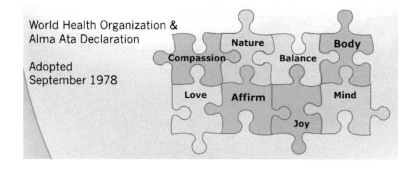

World Health Organization & Alma Ata Declaration

Adopted September 1978

Historical Antecedents:

- ## The Herbalist Charter

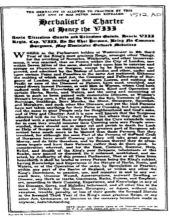

Translation: Were in the Parliament holden at Westminster in the third Year of the King's most gracious reign, amongst other things, for the avoiding of Sorceries, Witchcrafts, and other Inconveniences, it was enacted, that no Person within the City of London, nor within Seven Miles of the same, should take upon him to exercise and occupy as Physician or Surgeon, except he be first examined, approved, and admitted by the Bishop of London and other, under and upon certain Pains and Penalties in the same Act mentioned: Sithence the making of which said Act, the Company and Fellowship of Surgeons of London, minding only their own Lucres, and nothing the Profit or ease of the Diseased or Patient, have sued, troubled, and vexed divers honest Persons, as well Men as Women, whom God hath endued with the Knowledge of the Nature, Kind and Operation of certain Herbs, Roots, and Waters, and the using and ministring of them to such as been pained with customable Diseases, as Women's Breast's being sore, a Pin and the Web in the Eye, Uncomes of Hands, Burnings, Scaldings, Sore Mouths, the Stone, Strangury, Saucelim, and Morphew, and such other like Diseases; and yet the said Persons have not taken anything for their Pains or Cunning, but have ministered the same to poor People only for Neighborhood and God's sake, and of Pity and Charity: And it is now well known that the Surgeons admitted will do no Cure to any Person but where they shall be rewarded with a greater Sum or Reward that the Cure extendeth unto; for in case they would minister their Cunning unto sore People unrewarded, there should not so many rot and perish to death for Lack or Help of Surgery as daily do; but the greatest part of Surgeons admitted been much more to be blamed than those Persons that they troubled, for although the most Part of the Persons of the said Craft of Surgeons have small Cunning yet they will take great sums of Money, and do little therefore, and by Reason thereof they do oftentimes impair and hurt their Patients, rather than do them good. In consideration whereof, and for the Ease, Comfort, Succour, Help, Relief, and Health of the King's poor Subjects, Inhabitants of this Realm, now pained or diseased: Be it ordained, established, and enacted by Authority of this present Parliament, That at all Time from henceforth it shall be lawful to every Person being the King's subject. having Knowledge and Experience of the Nature of Herbs, Roots, and Waters, or of the Operation of the same, by Speculation or Practice, within any part of the Realm of England, or within any other the King's Dominions, to practice, use, and minister in and to any outward Sore, Uncome Wound, Apostemations, outward Swelling or Disease, any Herb or Herbs, Ointments, Baths, Pultess, and Emplaisters, according to their

41

Cunning, Experience, and Knowledge in any of the Diseases, Sores, and Maladies beforesaid, and all other like to the same, or Drinks for the Stone, Strangury, or Agues, without suit, vexation, trouble, penalty, or loss of their goods; the foresaid Statute in the foresaid Third Year of the King's most gracious Reign, or any other Act, Ordinance, or Statutes to the contrary heretofore made in anywise, notwithstanding.

- **Part of our Common Law**

- **An Act of Henry the Eighth in the 33rd. Reign Year 1542**

- "Annis Tircesimo Quarto and Tricesimo Quinto. Henry VIII Regis. Cap. VIII. An Act That Persons, Being No Common Surgeons, May Administer Outward Medicines"

- To protect the "alternative Practitioners of the day from the newly government licensed Physicians

- Provides Freedom from "Suit, vexation, trouble, penalty, or loss of their goods…"

- **NOTE:** Under the General Laws of the Colonies taken over by the U.S.A., these rights are still in force in the original thirteen states and have **never been repealed**.

• Informed Consent

Based on common practices and international law encoded in the:

- Declaration of Helsinki (World Medical Association 1964-2008 revisions)

- UN, Universal Declaration of Human Rights (UDHR Article 18)
  - Everyone has the right to freedom of thought, conscience and religion; this right includes freedom to change his religion or belief, and freedom, either alone or in community with others and in public or private, to manifest his religion or belief in teaching, practice, worship and observance only with the permission of the person and not by force.

- The IACHR: American Declaration of the Rights and Duties of Man (Article III)
  - Every person has the right freely to profess a religious faith, and to manifest and practice it both in public and in private.

- The Pan American Health Organization Declaration of Alma-Ata (Article I- X)

- Based on common practices and international law encoded in the undersigned client hereby grants a Private License to the (Modality) Research/ Ecclesiastical Practitioner to engage in (Modality) and or Nutritional consultation with the under signed as expressive association activities. The undersigned acknowledges that the Practitioner is not a licensed medical doctor. The undersigned has been advised to seek the services of a physician in any medical condition is suspected.

- The Terms of a standard Informed Consent: "The undersigned acknowledges that the practitioner does not diagnose or prescribe for medical or psychological conditions nor claim to prevent, treat, mitigate or cure such conditions, to provide diagnosing, treating, operating or prescribing for any human disease, pain, injury, deformity or physical condition as defined in secular state medical practices acts."

- The Practitioner does not provide diagnosis, care, treatment or rehabilitation of individuals, nor does the Practitioner apply medical, mental health, or human development principles, as defined in State or other secular law or statute, but rather provides (Religious Therapeutics i.e. SomaVeda®) and or Nutritional. Mental, Emotional, Psychological consultation that may offer spiritual therapeutic benefit for the individual. Any nutrients or traditional remedies recommended may be obtained from any provider of such products.

- The undersigned gives Informed Consent for the (Modality), nutritional or other consultation and services that will be provided. The research information developed by the Practitioner may be used for research and publication with personal identification removed.

- Please see the standardized NAIC Inc. Disclaimer, Contract for Services, Membership and Informed Consent forms from NAIC provider.

NAIC, INC./ (Auxiliary/ Afilliate Name.) _____
PRIVATE MEMBER ACTIVITY INFORMED CONSENT, DISCLOSURE AND DISCLAIMER FORM

I request that (Authorized NAIC minister/ provider name: _____) perform Native American, Indigenous traditional Religious Therapeutic: Healing and or related: (SomaVeda® Thai Yoga/ Indigenous, Indigenous Traditional Thai Massage/ Nuad Boran, Jap Sen Nuat, Tapping, Ayurveda, Yoga, Tantra and or sacred expression of natural healing in session, evaluation, therapy, consultation, etc.) and to set up program/ programs (or have sessions, etc.) for the purpose of (counseling, educating, sharing, expressing and/ or practicing Religious Therapy: Native American Medicine, Ritual, Ceremony, Medicine/ Healing and or related indigenous, traditional earth based healing modalities such as Ayurveda, Yoga, Yoga therapy, SomaVeda® Thai Yoga, Indigenous Traditional Thai Yoga, Traditional Chinese Medicine, Nature Cure, Traditional Naturopathy, sharing/ expressing of love, compassion, joy and equanimity, as well as conversations regarding our mutual physical, mental, emotional or spiritual health and wellness including diet and any appropriate exchanges mutually agreed upon, using established procedures and methods approved by the Native American Indigenous Church, Inc. DBA NAIC, Inc.). I understand that religious therapeutic sessions may or may not involve ceremony, prayer, physical pressure (annointing) and facilitated movement, laying on of hands (Chirothesia), emotional, mental, psychological and spiritual counseling and/ or exercises.

I understand that (provider name: _____) has a (certification, degree, religious authorization or training) from NAIC: The Thai Yoga Center, or recognized NAIC seminary/ school located in state of Florida or school/ Minister, Certified Teacher approved by NAIC, Inc . I understand that any of the sacred healing practices (religious therapeutics) we share (sacredotal duties) and or express in private, are not intended as diagnosis, prescription, or treatment for any disease, physical or mental as defined by relevant state medical and or Massage/ Massage Therapy practices acts. It is also not intended as a substitute for regular medical care by a licensed medical provider.

I understand that all services / expressions regardless of the names or titles used to describe them: Aboriginal/ Indigenous Healing, Native American Healing Medicine, Ceremony, Sacraments, SomaVeda Integrated Traditional Therapies® Thai Yoga, Indigenous Traditional Thai Massage, Pancha Karma, Classical Ayurveda, meditations, affirmations, energy exchanges, prayers, Yoga practices, therapies, sessions, protocols, Bio-Tapp/ EFT and or other sacred indigenous, traditional, natural, non-invasive, holistic practices and healing conversations are private practices conducted by authorized members of Private Religious Domain and Private Religious Membership Organization: NAIC, Inc of which I am a member, and that I am NOT receiving these above referenced services as a member of the public. I understand that NAIC, Inc. is a Private Religious/ Church Domain, Private, Religious, Tribal Organization for the preservation, establishment and practise of Religious Therapeutics, Native American, Indigenous (aboriginal) Traditional Medicine and Therapies, Reiki, Energy Balancing, Spiritual Counseling and/ or related health, wellness and healing arts and sciences. In receiving these services I agree to abide by NAIC Articles of Religious practice, education and Healthcare Membership, NAIC Code of Ethics, NAIC Cancellation and Refund Policy as posted on church website SomaVeda.Com.

I understand that I do not need to be of Native American (aboriginal) heritage of origin to participate and or receive services from an NAIC Tribal organization authorized member/ provider/ minister/ therapist/ counselor. Access to Healing is a Human Right.

I am an adult, aged 21 or older, or a parent of a minor child, legally and mentally competent to make informed decisions regarding my beliefs, spiritual practices, health, wellness and recreation. I swear that all information provided by me in support of receiving/ participating in services from the above referenced practitioner are correct and true as a precondition towards participating in any private membership activities.

NINTH AMENDMENT DECLARATION : ARTICLE IX, U.S. CONSTITUTION
"The enumeration in the Constitution, of certain rights, shall not be construed to deny or disparage others retained by the People." Under the Ninth Amendment to the Constitution of the United States of America, I retain the right to freedom of choice in health care (or psychological services, or educational services, etc...). This includes the right to choose my diet, and to obtain, purchase and use any therapy, regimen, modality, remedy or product recommended by the fellow member, therapist, doctor or any practitioner and or religious provider of my choice. The enumeration in this declaration of these rights shall not be construed to deny or disparage other rights retained by me, or my right to amend this declaration at any time.

CONSTRUCTIVE NOTICE
Notice is hereby given to any person who receives a copy of this Declaration and who, acting under the color of law, intentionally interferes with the free exercise of the rights retained by me under the Ninth Amendment, as enumerated in this declaration, that they may be in violation of my civil and constitutional rights, Title 42, U.S.C. 1983 et seq. and Title 18, Section 241.

Print NAIC Members Name: _____   Date: _____ / _____ / _____

Members Signature: _____   NAIC Provider Initial: _____

Legal Exemptions from Medical Licensing

You may be exempt from State / Federal requirements for Medical Licensing by statute!

For Example: IF:

- You're an Ordained Medicine Man or Women, Ecclesiastical/ Pastoral Medical Therapists or Doctor from an established and legally cognizable church (Priory of Saving Grace/ NAIC), denomination, or sect and the Clerical Medical Services you're providing are within your accountable, standardized approved scope of practice and procedures.

Then:

- Your exempt from State and Federal Medical Licensing Laws and Registrations including so called "Massage Laws" due to #1

Most states actually have exemptions to mandatory medical licensing for Native tribal, Ecclesiastical/ Pastoral/ Ministerial Providers.

Legal Exemptions Are Not Loopholes!

Definition of Loophole:
    "A loophole is an ambiguity in a system, such as a law or security, which can be used to circumvent or otherwise avoid the intent, implied or explicitly stated, of the system."

Definition of Exemption/ Exception:
    The process of freeing or state of being free from an obligation or liability imposed on others: exemption from prescription charges | regulatory exemptions.
      • (includes personal exemption)

Example: Florida State Medical Board

1) **State Medical Statute Title XXXII chapter 490 "Psychological Services" Section 490.014 Exemptions.**

•   (f) Is a *rabbi, priest, minister, or member of the clergy of any religious denomination or sect* when engaging in activities which are within the scope of the performance of his or her regular or specialized ministerial duties and for which no separate charge is made, or when such activities are performed, with or without charge, for or under the auspices or sponsorship, individually or in conjunction with others, of an established and legally cognizable church, denomination, or sect, and when the person rendering service remains accountable to the established authority thereof.

2) State Medical Statute Title XXXII chapter 458
"Medical Practice "Section 458.303 Provisions not applicable to other practitioner; exceptions, etc. (e)☐ Any person furnishing medical assistance in case of an emergency. (f)☐ The domestic administration of recognized *family remedies*. (g) The practice of the religious tenets of any church in this state.

Our NAIC Indigenous Native Tribal Organization, our membership and Church is a family!

☐ "The practice of the religious tenets of any church in this state."

Ecclesiastical/ Church/ Religious Authorities and Jurisdictions have the clear right and authority to issue Medical and Clinical Licensing and or Commissions and Authorizations!

☐ The key seems to be: *or when such activities are performed, with or without charge, for or under the auspices or sponsorship, individually or in conjunction with others, **of an established and legally cognizable church, denomination, or sect, and when the person rendering service remains accountable to the established authority thereof.***

More Examples:

What if I told you that Christian Science practitioners are classified as "medical practitioners" by the government, and services provided by them are deductible on the patient's income tax return just like any physician's charges. Read the following and keep in mind that the government (State or federal) is restrained from discriminating between religions!

See how well this works for Clerical/ Pastoral/ Ecclesiastical/ Ministerial practitioners!

Medical expenses may include: Fees paid to doctors, dentists, surgeons, chiropractors, psychiatrists, psychologists, and **Christian Science practitioners** for medical care expenses: **http://www.irs.gov/taxtopics/tc502.html**

You can include in medical expenses fees you pay to Christian Science practitioners for medical care. http://www.irs.gov/publications/p502/ar02.html - en_US_publink1000178918

The Gov't cannot discriminate! The rights it extends to one church/ ecclesiastical/ religious organization are shared by all!

Conditions of Practice:

If your planning on practicing under the ecclesiastical exemptions / exceptions then:

1) You will need to join and have an active membership with an ecclesiastical, church/ religious organization/ Tribal Organization
2) The Church/ Tribal Org. provides ministerial medical/ healing training and a cogent, definable scope of practice, which clearly follows guidelines as, established by that authority/ jurisdiction.
3) You and Your practice and ministry it's self will have to be authorized directly and remain under the authority of the church/ tribal org. as long as you practice.
4) Your client/ communicants themselves will also be members of the Church/ Tribal Org.

An authorization or ministers/ ordination and or Medicine Person/ Practitioner is not a FREE Pass or Get Out of Jail Card!

Your practice must be an authentic representative of the **firmly held** beliefs of your church and yourself.

Organizations which recognize, authorize and support SomaVeda Integrated Traditional Therapies®:

- Eastern Apostolic Orthodox Catholic Church of the Americas, Chaldean- Syrian Rite

- Priory of Saving Grace (www.priorysg.org)

- SMOCH (Sacred Medical Order Church of Hope) (www.smoch.org)

- Native American Indigenous Church (NAIC)

- Association of Ayurveda Practitioner of North America (AAPNA)(www.aapna.org)

Private Membership Association

You also have rights as a member of a private membership association!

You can now legally practice-your profession in a First and Fourteenth Amendment Private Health or Medical Membership Association such as the Native American Indigenous Church Inc. (NAIC Inc.). This means that your membership association is outside the jurisdiction and authority of all state and federal agencies and law enforcement authorities.

This right is not absolute, but your association would have to be operating in the realm of a clear and present danger of substantive evil thus providing a compelling interest standard in order to trigger an investigation. In other words, there should be no concern of being subject to an injunction or criminal charges of practicing Religious Therapeutics, Chirothesia, health, healing, therapy, anointing, Massotherapy, Hatha Yoga, Indigenous Yoga Therapy, Traditional Ayurveda, Oriental Medicine, Sacred Naturopathy, Indigenous Traditional Thai Yoga and/or Traditional Thai Massage (ITTM) etc. without a secular *State, Municipal) license by law enforcement when practicing your profession within a Private Health or Medical Membership Association only with private members, not public patients or clients.

This is important, these legal protections ONLY occur when you're working on or with other church/ NAIC members!

First, an understanding of the difference between a mala in se crime and a *mala prohibita crime is important. mala in se crime is a "crime or evil in itself," e.g. murder, rape, bank robbery, etc. even under common law.*

A mala prohibita crime is not a "crime in itself" but is only a crime because a state legislature or federal congress makes it a crime for the public welfare. For example, the federal government or a state may decide to license a certain profession that was legal to do before licensing. After the licensing statute, a person who conducts that profession without a license could be charged with a felony or misdemeanor criminal offense for practicing without a license.

EXAMPLE: In the public domain, a person who advises another that his legal rights have been infringed and refers him to a particular attorney has committed a mala prohibita felony crime in the State of Virginia. But in the private domain of a First Amendment legal membership association, the state, "...in the domain of these indispensable liberties, whether of... association, the decisions of this Court recognize that abridgment of such rights." N.A.A.C.P. v. Button, 371 U.S. 415 at 421. The "modes of...association protected by the First and Fourteenth (are modes) which Virginia may not prohibit. N.A.A.C.P. v. Button, at 415.

In other words, a private mode or domain is protected and is a different domain than a public domain.

What was a *mala prohibita felony criminal act in the public domain became a legally protected act in the private domain or private association.*

Mala in se crime (is a "crime or evil in itself,") is not legally protected in the private domain or private association.

All this means that you can practice all forms of healing arts without a license within your Private Therapeutic Membership Association of church/ private members!

Also, the private domain is referred to as a "sancta from unjustified interference by the State" in Pierce v. Society of Sisters, 268 U.S. 510 at 534-535. And as a "constitutional shelter" in Roberts v. United States, 82 L.Ed.2d 462 at 472. And again as a "shield" in Robberts v. United States, supra at 474. In addition, the U.S. Supreme Court in Thomas v. Collins, 323 U.S. 516 at 531, specifically refers to the "Domains set apart...for free assembly." The First Amendment right to association creates a 'preserve" Baird v. Arizona, 401 U.S. 1. The private domain of an association is a sanctuary, constitutional shelter, shield, and domain set apart and a preserve according to a number of U.S. Supreme Court decisions. Again, your Private Therapeutic Membership Association of private members is in the private domain with the protection of numerous favorable U.S. Supreme Court decisions with none to the contrary to date.

Ethics and Practice

- Ethical Considerations center on:

  - Informed Consent

  - Authorization, Ordination and or Licentiate/ Commission to serve/ Counsel

  - Sacerdotal, Ceremonial, Religious Therapeutic Services Between NAIC/ Church Members

  - Code of Conduct

Chirothesia Practitioners Code:

- Do No Harm

- Honor and Respect the client/ communicant at all times

- Work with Informed Consent

- Work on the Whole Person

- Work on Your Self for the benefit of others

- Honor Your Predecessors, Ancestors, Elders

- All work is an extension of Spirit, Vitality, Prayer and Breath

Structuring Your Practice

- **All** Clients join NAIC (and or NAIC Authorized Independent Branch) as APM (Authorized Blessed Participant Members or equivalent)

- **Only and exclusively serve Member/ Communicants and only work on Member/ Communicants.**

- Have those you serve to join church or if serving a public need have them sign the *NAIC Waiver and Consent form.*

- Home Office? Check with your homeowner's insurance agency for a professional home office rider for religious ministry.

- Business License? The *Religious Land Use and Institutionalized Persons Act of 2000 (RLUIPA)* establishes your right to conduct and practice ceremony and healing without permission of any secular governmental agency.

- Churches and Ministers do not generally need Liability Insurance if practicing ethically and according to scope of education and practice by private agreement.

- You may need to file for a Religious Exception in your county or city to notify them that you are operating a religious ministry out of a home or office. That's legal, however, they cannot deny you the right to practice your ministry!

- Become a Member of NAIC, Inc.

- (and/ or NAIC Authorized Independent Branch)

- Join NAIC an AFM (Authorized Full Participant) and or AFM (Authorized Open Participant) Card

- ($200.00 Suggested Donation)

- Tithe 10% of your net income to support the NAIC Tribal Organization. Most if not all churches ask for Tax Deductable donations to support the ministry, offices and infrastructure as well as maintenance and or expansion. More or less as your led.

Your Web and Internet Use

- Internet Presence and Use- Risk / Benefit
- Using Language on the Internet
- Meta-Tags and Hidden Text
- Third Party Links (Add links from your website, page etc. to…)

  - **SomaVeda.Com (Official NAIC Website)**

  - **SomaVeda.Org (Official SomaVeda College of Natural Medicine Site)**

  - **ThaiYogaCenter.Com (SCNM: School of Ayurveda and Natural Medicine)**

  - **PriorySG.Org** (Priory of Saving Grace: Official Parent NAIC organization website)

  - **BeardedMedia.Com** (NAIC Book and Materials Store)

  - **ThaiMassage.Com** (Indigenous Traditional Thai Medicine and Traditional Thai Yoga (Thai Massage slang articles and scientific research.)

FaceBook:

- **FaceBook.Com/LearnThaiYoga** (Official FB FanPage for Networking)
- **FaceBook.com/groups/914750425242849/** (US Thai Yoga Therapy Group)

- Set up a personal profile then a "FanPage". Put all of your marketing, business and practice info on the FanPage. "Friend" and "Like" Learn Thai Yoga Fan Page and then "Like" and Cross Post all of our post etc.

- Quoting Copyrighted Materials

  - **Always give credit where credit is due!** As long as you are an active enrolled student, NAIC Member you can quote from us with proper credit i.e. ©2019 Anthony B. James/ NAIC/ NAIC Inc./ Native American Indigenous Church / Priory of Saving Grace

- Always Use Proper Trademaks and or Logos

  - SomaVeda® Thai Yoga, SomaVeda Integrated Traditional Therapy®, SomaVeda® are a Federally Registered Trademark/ Service mark and proprietary Intellectual Property, All World Rights Reserved.

IMPORTANT! Always use the SomaVeda® and or Style name of what your practicing. AVOID using GENERIC terms to refer to your practice that do not accurately disclose the nature of your training, certification and authorization to practice. As a point of law, none of these referenced generic names are descriptive of something legal to practice. They can be and are confused with legally contentious words and terms now under authority of State Massage Licensing Boards and or soon to be "Yoga" Licensing boards if Yoga Alliance is successful in pushing this through!

Generic Questionable Examples are: *Thai Yoga, Thai Massage, Massage Therapy, Massage, Bodywork, Bodywork Therapy, Thai Bodywork, Thai Yoga Therapy, Thai Healing, Yoga Therapy, Reflexology, Thai Reflexology etc.*

Most secular licensing boards regulate the use of the words: massage, massage therapy, bodywork, deep tissue, full body massage, body massage, reflexology. Best practices are to avoid using them entirely. To be precise consult with the license laws in whatever state you reside and practice in.

A good resource, with some state by state opinions and references is found on the NAIC Church website: Legal Compliance: *http://www.somaveda.com/NAIC-legal-compliance/*

Acceptable Examples are SomaVeda®: ...
SomaVeda Integrated Traditional Therapies®:
          Thai Yoga
Thai Yoga,
Indigenous Thai Yoga,
Indigenous Traditional Thai Yoga,
Indigenous Thai Yoga Therapy,
Indigenous Traditional Thai Massage,
Thai Sacred Bodywork,
Thai Yoga Religious Therapy,
Thai Sacred Healing,
Thai Yoga Ayurveda (ALC and above only)
Thai Ayurveda Wellness Consultant (ALC- above only)
Thai Ayurveda Health Counselor (AHC- above only)
Thai Ayurveda Yoga Therapist (AYT- above only)
Ayurvedic Thai Yoga
Ayurvedic Thai Yoga Therapy
Therapeutic Yoga
Yoga Therapeutics,
Sacred Reflexology,
Sacred Thai Reflexology
Religious Therapeutics
Monastic Medicine

Pastoral Medicine
Pastoral Therapy
Native American Medicine (With NAIC Authorization only- AFM, LCHT, Ordained)
Native American Indigenous Medicine (With NAIC Authorization only- AFM, LCHT, Ordained)
Indigenous Traditional Medicine
Tribal Organization Health Care
NAIC Tribal Health Care
NAIC Tribal Wellness Services
Indigenous (clerical/ pastoral/ ministerial) Healthcare, Healing Science, Counseling and Medicine (IHSM)
Wellness Coach (ing) Service
Holistic Health Coach

etc.

In other words, if a lay public person was reading a description of the counseling and or religious therapies that your offering, they would be able to tell your offering **ministerial services** of healing!

Being proud of your training and the authority which protects your right to practice not only helps build public awareness of what we have to offer as spiritually based healing modalities but is essential to creating a legal umbrella under which you can safely practice and under which your patients and clients can safely and privately receive your services, counseling, advise and therapies.

EXAMPLE:

Description of business or practice: Indigenous Religious Therapeutics...
Offering Services such as:
SomaVeda Integrated Traditional Therapies® / and or **SomaVeda®...**

Indigenous Thai Yoga Therapy
Traditional Thai Yoga
Thai Yoga Therapy (AYT)
Sacred Thai Yoga
Sacred Thai Yoga Therapy (AYT)
Ayurveda Wellness Counseling (AWC)
Ayurveda Health Consultant (AHC)
Vedic Counseling
Native Counseling
Indigenous Services
Sacred Nutrition
Religious Therapeutics: Thai Yoga
Wellness Coaching
Holistic Health Coach etc.

SomaVeda® Indigenous (clerical/ pastoral/ ministerial) Healthcare, Healing Science, Counseling and Medicine (IHSM)

Every SomaVeda® Thai Yoga and or SomaVeda Integrated Traditional Therapies@ program of any kind is issued copies of SomaVeda®, SCNM, NAIC logos to use in promotional materials and internet use.

- Using Copyrighted Images:

    - Same as above... As an Authorized NAIC SomaVeda® Practitioner (Minister) you have

65

many resources to use for your practice, clinic, counseling and or healing services. See our Photo Galleries for Thousands of images to use in your marketing.

- You may use NAIC®, SomaVeda® Logo's, same criteria as above

- SUS - Site Use Statement
  For suggested wording go to:
  http://thaiyogacenter.com/general-information/privacy-policy

The Forbidden Words

Unless your using these words in a clearly evident ecclesiastical, religious, ministerial and counseling related manner, having identified yourself as an Authorized Ministerial Practitioner, Medicine Person and or Counselor... **DO NOT USE!**

Reserved Medical Terms:
> (Restricted in Secular not in Church, Religious Use)

- Diagnose
- Prescribe
- Treat (example: Massage/ Massage Therapy)
- Prevent
- Mitigate
- Cure
  - FDA "Structure and Function Rule
  - DSHEA Statutory Disclaimer "These statements have not been evaluated by the Food and Drug Administration. This product is not intended to diagnose, treat, cure or prevent any disease." (Must be present when recommending service or products)

PLEASE NOTE: However, if you have identified yourself as a minister, counselor and or medicine person, then OK!

Business License and or Special Exceptions Permits etc.

You have the right as a minister to express, practice and or share your healing work, counseling and ministry to suffering people anywhere. In fact, we order you to do so! No one can legally stop or interfere with this right legally.

Having said this does not automatically mean you might not have to have a business license or a special exception permit from a governmental agency. However, you do have a legal right to operate your ministry out of your home! You can share an office space. You can see your clients in a hospital setting... in fact anywhere a minister of any religion can go you can go. Anywhere any ministry of any kind can be you can be!

Your primary defense or argument is that you are an Authorized NAIC Minister practicing a healing ministry, a ministry of religious therapy and whatever that might entail based on your education and authorization from NAIC.

If you want to open a practice and create a church directly you can do that. You can apply for an NAIC Branch... to be an integrated Auxiliary of NAIC. If your intention is to build a clinic the we recommend you apply for Branch under both NAIC and Priory of Saving Grace. There are several State certified Medical Clinics operating right now under us. Please contact the office here separately if this process interest you.

However, you do not have to have a branch of your own to legally practice... we have already authorized this ministry level for you as a Certified Practitioner: NAIC Authorized Full Blessed Member.

Please note: DO NOT contact Massage Boards and the like to SEE if your legal! Massage Boards legitimately regulate the massage profession and have literally no knowledge of Religious therapeutics, Chirothesia, Sacred Yoga Therapy, Ayurveda, Indigenous, Traditional, Native, Aboriginal and or Natural Medicine. Since our practice is NOT massage/ massage therapy there is no reason they should be involved at all.

You are legal to practice SomaVeda® in all 50 states with no massage or other licensing!

The only way a state or government agency can require you to separately have a massage or other "Vocational" license is if you say that's what you do! No governmental agency can define your religious expressions and practices that you share with other church members.

Just so you can read this as it is a common question: Does it make any difference if I charge money or not in reference to needing a license? NO and absolutely NO. It matters not whether you charge or what you charge. All ministers are able to make a living by producing income.

File your taxes as minister! This also supports your claim to be practicing a ministry.

Liability Insurance?

Apparently massage is very dangerous and so most states require massage therapist to obtain expensive liability insurance. First of all since we are not doing massage what we do is not considered dangerous to anyone. In fact no one has ever died from receiving SomaVeda® Therapies... ever! You only work on other NAIC members. All NAIC Members as a precondition to joining the church sign and agree to all member conditions and responsibilities. They agree that your services are private, privileged and under church jurisdiction. They further agree that any and all claims of injury etc. will be presented to and decided by church arbitration process, no exceptions. As long as your practice is genuine, you work within your authorized scope of practice, you are protected from liability.

If you still want an independent liability policy, we can make recommendations... give us a call. We established recognition for SomaVeda® Thai Yoga with them years ago as a Yoga and or Yoga Therapy Somatic practice and you can get a policy from them... although, not necessary to do so.

We are committed to bring all of our relations into to harmony, balance and oneness as our Mother Earth based religious beliefs dictate.

What if I am a Licensed Massage Therapist or other Licensed Vocational and or Medical Professional currently?

It is vitally important that you do not collapse the healing work of NAIC SomaVeda Integrated Traditional Therapies®: Thai Yoga, Ayurveda etc. with the secular therapy practice. You must create distinctions. You must clearly separate your healing practice and clients as well. On a personal note of just how to do this, there are so many variations that we will want to speak to you directly to help formulate strategy and organizing. But essentially you can do any job and also work as an authorized ministry... you just have to keep them separate and distinctive from one another if your working under NAIC Legal umbrella.

Summary

Every practitioner of spirit, vitality, energy based holistic and/or Religious Therapeutic CAM therapies need to know the legal principles, which support or guide the practice.

Your healing ministry and the native religious therapeutic and or traditional medicinal practices and expressions, based on Indigenous, Tribal, Ecclesiastical, Religious, Familial traditions *must be evidenced by a sincere and firmly held conviction* and the doctrines and dogma's, published or oral as taught, conveyed and passed on to you by your Native American Indigenous Church, Native American Religious Tribal Organization or Religion.

As a professional, clerical, ministerial and or tribal org. authorized provider and or practitioner you should be prepared. You should be prepared to defend, apologize and or explain these beliefs to an uninformed person and or officer of some secular legal jurisdiction or any other person who might not be educated in Native American religious freedom and or church rights and law.

Uneducated and or misinformed persons will not be cognizant of your authorizations, rights, duties and responsibilities as a traditional practitioner of the Indigenous and Traditional Natural Medicine or medicines.
We are authorized to practice without undo interference, to represent, express, practice, manifest and share our indigenous healing and medicine freely with our families and

co-members and the world.

Please note the consequences of violating the **Religious Land Use and Institutionalized Person Act of 2000,**

Title 18, U.S.C., Section 242 Deprivation of Rights Under Color of Law

This statute makes it a crime for any person acting under color of law, statute, ordinance, regulation, or custom to willfully deprive or cause to be deprived from any person those rights, privileges, or immunities secured or protected by the Constitution and laws of the U.S. This law further prohibits a person acting under color of law, statute, ordinance, regulation or custom to willfully subject or cause to be subjected any person to different punishments, pains, or penalties, than those prescribed for punishment of citizens on account of such person being an alien or by reason of his/her color or race. Acts under "color of any law" include acts not only done by federal, state, or local officials within the bounds or limits of their lawful authority, but also acts done without and beyond the bounds of their lawful authority; provided that, in order for unlawful acts of any official to be done under "color of any law," the unlawful acts must be done while such official is purporting or pretending to act in the performance of his/her official duties. This definition includes, in addition to law enforcement officials, individuals such as Mayors, Council persons, Judges, Nursing Home Proprietors, Security Guards, etc., persons who are bound by laws, statutes ordinances, or customs. Punishment varies from a fine or imprisonment of up to one year, or both, and if bodily injury results or if such acts include the use, attempted use, or threatened use of a dangerous weapon, explosives, or fire shall be fined or imprisoned up to ten years or both, and if death results, or if such acts include kidnapping or an attempt to kidnap, aggravated sexual abuse or an attempt to commit aggravated sexual abuse, or an attempt to kill, shall be fined under this title, or imprisoned for any term of years or for life, or both, or may be sentenced to death

Priory of Saving Grace Inc., NAIC Inc, NAIC, SMOCH, SCNM and The Thai Yoga center support your rights as an Authorized member, practitioner of a bonafide Native American Tribal Organization and recognized Native American Church to practice as a legal and Human Right!

Aho!

Additional Law and Legal Considerations
http://www.somaveda.com/NAIC-legal-compliance/
More Information:

- SOMAVEDA.Com

- SOMAVEDA.ORG

- ThaiYogaCenter.Com

- SMOCH.Org

- PriorySG.Org

Bibliography

1. Indian Religious and Civil Freedoms Act (AIRFA)
The American Indian Religious and Civil Freedoms Act, Public Law No. 95-341, 92 Stat. 469 (Aug. 11, 1978) (commonly abbreviated to AIRFA), codified at 42 U.S.C. § 1996, http://www.somaveda.com/airfa/

2. IRS: Who must file: http://www.irs.gov/Charities-&-Non-Profits/Annual-Exempt-Organization-Return:-Who-Must-File

3. IRS Tax Guide for Churches: http://www.irs.gov/pub/irs-pdf/p1828.pdf

4. Religious Land Use and Institutionalized Persons Act of 2000 June 2, 2005, 106th CONGRESS, 2d Session S. 2869: http://www.somaveda.com/religious-act/

5. NAIC ARTICLES OF RELIGIOUS PRACTICE, EDUCATION AND HEALTHCARE MEMBERSHIP: http://www.somaveda.com/NAIC-articles-of-religious-practice-education-and-healthcare-membership/

6. NAIC Authorized Participant Membership Approval and Agreement: http://www.somaveda.com/NAIC-authorized-member-agreement/

7. State Medical and Massage Board Exemptions for Native, Ecclesiastical/ Religious/ Church Practitioners: http://www.somaveda.com/state-medical-and-massage-board-religious-exemptions/

8. PROVIDERS DECLARATION OF NINTH AMENDMENT RIGHTS: http://www.somaveda.com/ninth-amendment-declaration/

9. Gonzales vs. O Centro Espirita Beneficente União do Vegetal: http://udvusa.org/SupremeCourtDecision.pdf

10. The Boyl Decision: http://www.somaveda.com/the-boyll-decision/
11. NAIC Religious Tribal Organization Legal Rights Page: http://www.somaveda.com/onacs-legal-compliance/

12. State of Utah Supreme Court Unanimous Ruling, June 22, 2004: http://nativeamericanchurches.org/u-s-attorney-general-office-memorandum-to-the-dea/

13. UNITED STATES ATTORNEY GENERAL OFFICE – Memorandum to the Drug Enforcement Administration – 12/07/2000: http://nativeamericanchurches.org/u-s-attorney-general-office-memorandum-to-the-dea/

14. Leslie Fool Bull, N.A.C. Rosebud S.D. President – Take this Medicine to the White Man: http://nativeamericanchurches.org/take-this-medicine-to-the-white-man/

15. Confirmation of this Blessing and an additional Blessing by Richard 'He Who Holds the Foundation' Swallow: http://nativeamericanchurches.org/wp-content/uploads/2013/04/2nd.-Richard-Swallow-Blessing-August-19-2007.doc

16. Material Regarding OPM+: http://www.opm.gov/oca/fmla/fmla96.pdf http://www.opm.gov/oca/fmla/ http://uscode.house.gov/download/pls/25C18.txt

17. Mental Health http://us-code.vlex.com/vid/mental-prevention-treatment-services-19207699

18. Sec. 831. Traditional health care practices. http://www.house.gov/legcoun/Comps/IHCIA.pdf

19. Extensive, 2003 Congressional Record citation regarding Tribal Traditional Medicine Practices! http://books.google.com/books?id=rT9PtP4vR-0C&pg=PA5495&lpg=PA5495&dq=25+USC+13+(B)(4)+Utilization+and+promotion+of+Traditional+Indian+Health+Care+and+Treatment+Practices&source=bl&ots=2kFuEvCgRS&sig=-Fr3YzRaVIe941xe7MLhgEomrQ4&hl=en&sa=X&ei=DPWrUPmQGKSayQHV-4CwAw&ved=0CEoQ6AEwBA#v=onepage&q=25%20USC%2013%20(B)(4)%20Utilization%20and%20promotion%20of%20Traditional%20Indian%20Health%20Care%20and%20Treatment%20Practices&f=false

20. California information traditional healers http://www.calendow.org/uploadedfiles/principles_standards_cultural_competence.pdf

21. 5 USC 6381 (2)(B), the term 'Health Care Provider' includes Traditional Tribal (American Native Culture) Healing and Empower Practitioner (NAIC Medicine Person and/or Spiritual Leader). Note, the following designations are used by NAIC – Certified Traditional Tribal Healer (CTTH) or Certified Traditional Tribal Practitioner (CTTP) and said designated individuals are found on NAIC Spiritual Leader Registry. The CTTH designated Gatherings of providers pertains to those Healers and Empowers who's training & education pertains to counseling professionals, Indigenous American Native Spiritual Leaders trained in conducting Indigenous American Native Culture Ceremonies; Such as the Sacred Breath, Touch for Health (Holy Anointing), Sacred Prayer Pipe, Sacrament (Peyote), Sun Dance and Sweat Lodge spiritual practices.

Under 5 U.S.C. 6381(2)(B), OPM is authorized to designate any other health care provider who is determined by OPM to be capable of providing health care services. In response to these comments, OPM has revised the definition of "health care provider" to include a Native American, including an Eskimo, Aleut, and Native Hawaiian, who is recognized as a traditional healing practitioner by native traditional religious leaders and who practices traditional healing methods as believed, expressed, and exercised and in Indian religions of the American Indian, Eskimo, Aleut, and Native Hawaiians, consistent with the Native American Religious Freedom Act.:
http://www.ihs.gov/PublicAffairs/DirCorner/docs/IHCIA%20STATUS%20TABLE%204-5-12%20FINAL.pdf

22. 25 USC 13 (B)(4) – Utilization and promotion of Traditional Indian (Indigenous American Native Culture) Health Care and Treatment Practices: NAIC has its own system for certifying and registering designated Indigenous American Native Health Care Provider(s). Note: the Bureau of Indian Affairs (BIA), by 'does not' have any oversight concerns with NAIC

25 USC 18 § 1616 (b)(6) To promote Indigenous American Native Culture Health Care and Treatment Practices of the American Native Culture.

25 USC 18 § 1621 (a)(4)(D) The term of Native Medicine Man or Women will suffice for general public; but as with all American Native Cultures, not all Medicine Men or Women practice the full spectrum that tradition allows. NAIC has Gathering Programs and Spiritual Leader registry to recognize and authorize individuals at their achieved levels (Status) of Indigenous American Native Culture Health Care programs.

Note, *each NAIC entity registered or affiliated with NAIC is responsible and held accountable for ensuring that their American Native Culture Ceremonies and their Spiritual Leader's have achieved an approved Status through successfully completing NAIC Gathering Programs (ie., interns) and strictly adheres to NAIC Code of Ethics.*

23. Legal Guidelines /Jurisprudence and Business Ethics : Dr. Larry Wilson: http://beardedmedia.com/Legal-Guidelines-Jurisprudence-and-Business-Ethics-Book-NTB-20.htm

Made in the USA
San Bernardino, CA
29 February 2020